If you're a dog lover…

stop reading this book immediately, turn around and scamper away with your t
I'm surprised you can read at all. This book is not onl
because you lot have no sense of humour. We all know what you're like. You bark and bray, you like to be in charge, you like order, rules and military precision. You take your canine companions for brisk walks, which we all know provides you with cover for snooping on your neighbours. You think you're so great with your Telegraph subscription, your middle management jobs and your membership of the National Trust. We know you just like to be seen gadding about in the country, as if you care about the environment, when your Labrador poos all over it and scares away all the wildlife. You think you're the bees knees with your shooting jackets, your gumboots and your Land Rovers. Yes, even your cars sound like dogs. You have frightfully sensible names like Marjory and Sinjin Hackett-Sideboard. I'll probably receive a braying letter now, saying, "I come from a long line of Sideboards, all of whom kept cats. I, myself, have 19. I collect cat motif eggcups and have had myself spayed." But seriously folks, do keep in touch, if you've got anything to say about this book, cats, dogs or life in general. I might even print your correspondence in the next book. One thing though - don't write to tell me you like both cats AND dogs. This is like saying you support Arsenal AND Tottenham Hotspur, or that you take your tea with sugar AND without. Cat people and dog people are as different as chalk and cheese and they get on better with their own kind. I'm not saying we should build a big wall to separate the two species… Although, come to think of it…

Devil Cat

© 2012 Adrian Keefe   zoz261@yahoo.com   www.devil-cat.com   suzyandsooty.blogspot.co.uk   Devil Cat

 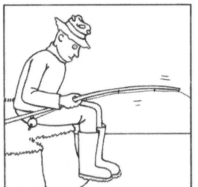 

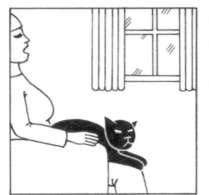

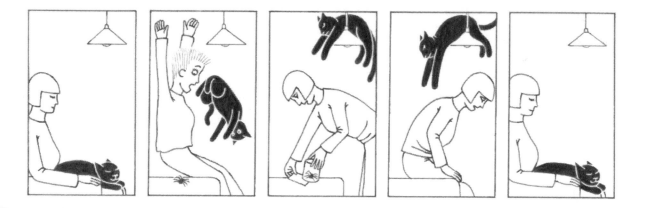

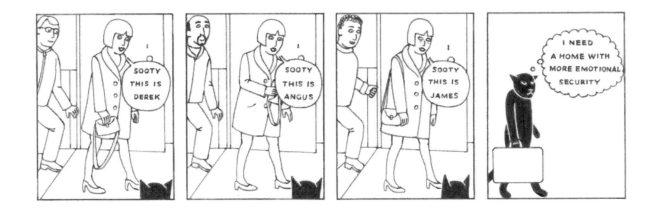